coke
or
pepsi?

Amazing!

coke
or
pepsi?

PASS THIS BOOK TO ALL
YOUR FRIENDS. EACH ONE CAN
ANSWER A SET OF REALLY
AWESOME QUESTIONS.

ARE YOU AND YOUR FRIENDS TOTALLY IN SYNC
OR COMPLETELY UNIQUE?
IT'S AN AMAZING WAY TO GET TO KNOW THEM!

10 Totally Amazi

WHERE WERE YOU BETWEEN
9AM & 10AM THIS MORNING?

○ COKE
○ PEPSi?

DO YOU BELIEVE iN
LOVE @
FIRST SiGHT? • NO
• YES

MOST-PRIZED POSSESSION?

FAVE PERK iF YOU WERE QUEEN?
• BODYGUARDS WATCHING MY BACK
• A DRIVER TO TAKE ME EVERYWHERE
• SUBJECTS BOWING DOWN

• UNTiE
• KiCK OFF
SNEAKERS?

Questions 4

NAME

LAST REALLY FUN → THING YOU DID?

WHAT DO YOU LIKE DAYDREAMING ← ABOUT?

- LOVING THE COOL LIFE INSIDE
- CRAVING THE ADVENTURE OF THE GREAT OUTDOORS?

SCREAM OUT LOUD ON ROLZERCOASTERS?

- YES!
- NO

coke or pepsi?

NAME YOUR FRIENDS CALL YOU?

1. SONG YOU GET STUCK iN YOUR HEAD?

2. IF YOU WERE A DJ, WHAT KiND OF MUSiC WOULD YOU PLAY?

3. FAVE WAY TO DiSCOVER NEW MUSiC?

4. SONG YOU ALWAYS GET UP AND DANCE TO?

5. SONG YOU CAN'T STAND?

6. Fave text abbreviation?

7. Least fave text abbreviation?

8. WEAR GREEN ON ST. PATRICK'S DAY?
○ ALWAYS ○ SOMETIMES ○ NEVER

9. One word to describe your BFF?

_____

10. WHAT'S MORE FUN? ○ SLEEPOVER ○ PARTY

11. DO YOU KNOW HOW TO YO-YO?
○ YES ○ KIND OF ○ NO

12. ○ Picnic in the park ○ Fun night out?

13. Worst chore ever? _____

14. Watch anything last night? ○ No ○ Yes, _____

15. Playground game you miss? _____

16. Are you more ○ emotional ○ logical ○ 50/50?

17. WOULD YOU DESCRIBE YOURSELF AS ○ EXTROVERTED ○ INTROVERTED ○ IN THE MIDDLE?

18. How would your family describe you? _____

_____

19. CELEBRITY YOU'RE THE MOST LIKE? _____

20. If you could, what would you splurge on? _____

_____

coke or pepsi?

NAME

1. **NAME YOU** WISH YOU HAD?

2. ○ I'M THE QUEEN OF
   ○ ENOUGH WITH THE
   ○ OTHER _____
   SELFIES?

3. ○ MAC ○ PC?

4. IF YOUR PET COULD TALK, **WHAT 3 QUESTIONS WOULD YOU ASK IT?**

CHECK OUT MY NEW SHADES!

5. DOES YOUR PET HAVE A COOL TRICK OR SWEET HABIT?

6. CELEB YOU'D LOVE AS YOUR OTHER BFF? _____

7. Vacation ○ in the big city ○ warm beach ○ another country?

8. Family's favorite meal? _____

9. Waffles with ○ strawberries & whipped cream ○ butter & maple syrup?

10. Best thing on your bedroom walls? _____

11. Ever been a member of a fan club? ○ No ○ Yes, _____

12. DO YOU HAVE A CELEBRITY AUTOGRAPH? ○ NO ○ YES, _____

13. Favorite song to sing with friends?

14. ○ Fast food ○ Themed restaurant ○ Fine dining?

15. FAVE VEGGIE?

16. Do your friends love your
○ sense of humor
○ talent
○ style?

17. Poetry is
○ awesome
○ OK
○ so boring?

18. Tell people there's food stuck in their teeth?
○ Never ○ Depends ○ Always

19. Something you do really fast? _____

20. Is your dream machine a(n)
○ limo with driver ○ SUV
○ sports car ○ hybrid?

NAME

WHO HAS IT EASIER?
• GiRLS
• BOYS
☞ WHY?

HOW MANY PAIRS OF SHOES DO YOU OWN?
• NOT ENOUGH   • JUST RIGHT   • TOO MANY!

SOMETHING YOU ♥ THAT MOST PEOPLE HATE?

WHAT'S YOUR BEST HABIT?

STUDY
• iN A QUIET PLACE
• WiTH MUSiC iN MY EARS
• WiTH TV ON?

HOW ARE YOU WHEN WAiTiNG iN LONG LiNES?

○ COOL ○ iRRiTATED ○ i WALK AWAY!

FAVE SNEAKER COLOR?

○ ● ○ ● ○ ● ○ ● ○ ●

OTHER _____

EVER BEEN ON TV?
○ NOPE ○ YES,

_____

TV SHOW THAT WOULD BE FUN TO ★ iN?

_____

LAST SiTCH WHiCH REALLY UPSET YOU?

EVER BELIEVE A MONSTER WAS UNDER YOUR BED?
○ YES
○ NO

FAVE FREE-TiME THiNG TO DO?

_____

LAST MOViE YOU SAW? _____

FAVE JUNK FOOD?

FAVE SUPER HEALTHY FOOD?

MOST BORiNG BOOK YOU'VE EVER READ?

_____

HARD TO SAY YOU'RE SORRY?
● YES
● SOMETiMES
● NO

GO-TO MOViE FOOD?
○ POPCORN ○ TWiZZLERS
○ NACHOS ○ OTHER

_____

coke or pepsi?

NAME

1. SOMETHING YOU'RE PROUD OF?

2. CHOPSTICKS?
○ SO FUN!
○ SO ANNOYING!
○ FORK, PLEASE.

3. FICTIONAL PLACE YOU'D LOVE TO VISIT?

4. WOULD YOU KISS A FROG IF YOU KNEW IT WOULD TURN INTO A HANDSOME PRINCE?
○ SURE! ○ NO WAY!

5. WHAT'S YOUR TYPICAL SUNDAY MORNING?

6. Favorite craft to make? _____

7. SCARED OF HEIGHTS? ○ YES! ○ NO ○ DEPENDS HOW HIGH.

8. Scared of spiders? ○ Ahh! Yes! ○ Nope

9. __ Finding a leprechaun __ Finding his pot of gold?

10. ○ Chocolate cake with chocolate ganache ○ Angel food cake with berries?

11. Jewelry you always wear? _____

12. Word you always misspell? _____

13. What or who totally amazes you?

14. ○ Long road trip ○ Short flight to your destination?

15. WHICH IS MORE EXCITING? ○ GRAMMYS ○ OSCARS

16. Ever entered a competition? ○ No ○ Yes, _____

17. VACATION IN ○ THE USA ○ AN EXOTIC LOCATION?

18. What would be a fun business to start?

19. Chew gum? ○ No ○ Yes, I love

20. Who's your favorite superhero?

 coke or pepsi?

NAME ON YOUR BIRTH CERTIFICATE?

1. DAY, DATE & TIME
YOU WERE BORN?

2. SOMETHING MOST PEOPLE DON'T KNOW ABOUT YOU?

3. WHAT DO YOU DO
WHEN YOU'RE

MAD?

● YELL ● CRY ● GET QUIET

4. WHO DO YOU SPILL YOUR GUTS TO?

5. ● MAKE QUICK DECISIONS
   ● THINK ABOUT IT
   ● AVOID DECISION-MAKING?

6. ○ TACO ○ BURRITO ○ ENCHILADA ○ FAJITA?

SAUCE ME!

7. Which is worse? ○ Paper cut ○ Burning your tongue

8. LAST THING YOU WROTE ABOUT? _____

9. Are you a hat girl? ○ No ○ Yes, I own_____ hats.

10. **What would you do with an extra hour every day?**

11. What's a typical Saturday for you? _____

12. First word you said? _____

13. Weirdest thing in your backpack or bag?

14. ○ Early ○ Right on time ○ Late to class?

15. Best memory you have? _____

16. What do you always lose? ○ socks ○ ponytail holders ○ pens

17. ○ Rays of sunshine on your face ○ Cool breeze in the shade?

18. Language you'd like to learn?

19. If you found $50, would you ○ save it ○ spend it ○ try to find its owner?

20. EVER FLOWN IN A HELICOPTER? ○ NO ○ YES, _____

coke or pepsi?

ALL THE NAMES YOU GO BY?

ONE WORD TO DESCRIBE YOURSELF?

THREE WORDS TO DESCRIBE GIRLS?

1.

2.

3.

MOST MAGICAL?
- PEGASUS • UNICORN
- DRAGON • OTHER ↓

- ROCK STAR
- STARFISH
- SHOOTING STAR?

FAVORITE SONG FROM A MOVIE?

READ ANYTHING GOOD LATELY?
- NOT REALLY • OH YEAH, IT'S

- CHOCOLATE • PRETZELS
- CHOCOLATE-COVERED PRETZELS?

WHAT'S OUTSIDE THE WINDOW CLOSEST TO YOU?

CAN YOU WHISTLE A TUNE?

- ○ YES
- ○ A LITTLE BIT
- ○ NO

THREE WORDS TO DESCRIBE BOYS?

1.
2.
3.

WHAT KIND OF STUDENT ARE YOU?
- ○ GOOD ○ GREAT
- ○ COULD BE BETTER

- ○ MOUNTAIN CLIMBING
- ○ HIKING TRAILS
- ○ S'MORES AROUND A CAMPFIRE?

TRAMPOLINES?
- ○ YES, LOVE THEM!
- ○ NO WAY!

EVER BEEN PRANKED? ○ NO ○ YES,

WHO MAKES YOU LAUGH THE HARDEST?

WEIRDEST MOVIE YOU'VE SEEN?

SOMETHING YOU'RE OBSESSED WITH?

WHAT DRIVES YOU CRAZY?

WHAT MAKES YOU FEEL REALLY LOVED?

coke
or
pepsi?

NAME

1. WHAT'S ON YOUR CALENDAR THIS WEEK?

2. LAST THING YOU COOKED, MICROWAVED, OR TOASTED?

3. FAVORITE
ROOM IN YOUR HOME?

4. HOW DO YOU LIKE TO
DECORATE?

5. WHAT'S YOUR FASHION STYLE?

6. EVER WEAR YOUR FRIENDS' CLOTHES?   ○ NOT REALLY   ○ ⊙H YEAH

7. SPRINKLES & GLITTER
   ○ MAKE EVERYTHING FUN ○ ARE ANNOYING & MESSY?

8. Who encourages you the most? _____

9. Staying organized ○ is so helpful ○ messes up creativity?

10. Something you wish you were good at? _____
_____

11. SOMETHING NEW YOU'VE LEARNED? _____

12. Favorite holiday treat? _____

13. Eggnog? ○ Love it! ○ So gross!

14. Celebrity wardrobe you'd love to borrow from?
_____

15. Are you squeamish? ○ Totally ○ Nah

16. ARE YOU AN ADVENTUROUS EATER? ○ YES ○ NO

17. CAMPING STYLE? ○ TENT ○ CABIN ○ RV

18. Ever encountered a wild animal?

○ No ○ Yes, _____

19. Favorite amusement park?

_____

20. Are you having a
○ good ○ bad ○ horrible hair day?

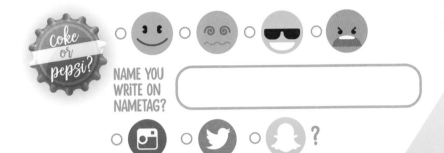

Coke or pepsi?

NAME YOU WRITE ON NAMETAG?

?

1. WHAT WOULD YOU DO WITH $1,000 IN ONE DAY?

2. DO YOU LIKE BEING IN THE SPOTLIGHT? ○YES ○NO

3. WHAT MAKES YOU LOSE TRACK OF TIME?

4. ○SOUR CREAM ○BARBEQUE ○CHEDDAR ○OTHER CHIPS?

5. WHAT DO YOU DO IN YOUR SPARE TIME?

MR. MEOW, WHAT SHOULD I WEAR TO THE DANCE?

6. DO YOU TALK TO YOUR PET LIKE IT'S A PERSON? ○ OF COURSE! ○ NAH

7. DO FRIENDS COUNT ON YOU FOR ○ PEP TALKS ○ REALITY CHECKS ○ SOME LAUGHS?

8. Fave game of all time? _____

9. Best band ever? _____

10. Favorite book character? _____

11. How many times do you hit Snooze in the morning? _____

12. FOOD YOU LOVE TO SMELL COOKING? _____

13. Where are you right now? _____

14. Where would you rather be? _____

15. Do you ○ think about the past ○ dream about the future more?

16. Have you ever been lost in a corn maze? ○ No ○ Yes!

17. Rather have a friend who ○ totally gets you ○ is tons of fun?

18. WHO DO YOU LOOK UP TO? _____

19. Ever fallen asleep in the middle of something? ○ No ○ Yes,

_____

20. Chocolate & ○ peanut butter ○ marshmallows ○ coconut?

coke or pepsi?

MY NAME is

I WISH MY NAME WERE

LITTLE KIDS ARE
○ FUN
○ ANNOYING?

FAMOUS PERSON YOU WOULD TRADE PLACES WITH?

....

WHAT'S BETTER?
○ ASKING QUESTIONS
○ GIVING ANSWERS

FAMOUS PERSON YOU'D NEVER TRADE PLACES WITH?

....

EVER BEEN EMBARRASSED BY YOUR PARENTS?
● NO ● YES
☞

SMARTEST PERSON YOU KNOW?

● COMFY
● TRENDY
SHOES?

IF YOU COULD INVENT SOMETHING, WHAT WOULD IT BE?

RULES SHOULD BE

○ FOLLOWED ○ USED AS GUIDELINES ○ BROKEN?

WORST FASHION MISTAKE YOU'VE EVER MADE?

○ PAY NOW PLAY LATER
○ PLAY NOW PAY LATER?

STUDY
○ ALONE
○ WITH A FRIEND
○ IN A GROUP?

BEST THING ABOUT SCHOOL?

MOST ANNOYING THING ABOUT SCHOOL?

MOST OUTRAGEOUS THING YOU'VE EVER EATEN?

WRITE papers
• IN ADVANCE
• THE NIGHT BEFORE?

coke or pepsi?

FIRST NAME

1. STORY BEHIND YOUR FIRST NAME? ● NO ● YES

2. IF YOU COULD GO TO ONLY ONE CONCERT THIS YEAR, WHICH WOULD IT BE?

3. ● PAY ATTENTION TO LYRICS
● JUST ROCK OUT TO THE MUSIC
● BOTH?

4. HOW WOULD YOUR FRIENDS DESCRIBE YOU?
● SWEET   ● RELIABLE   ● A LITTLE CRAY-CRAY?

5. EVER BEEN IN A PLAY? ● NO ● YES

6. Are you good at telling jokes? ○ Yes ○ No

7. Which would be fun to play? ○ Damsel in distress ○ Spy ○ Supervillain

8. Biggest question about life? _____

9. Have a fave cartoon? ○ Nope ○ Yep. _____

10. BEST CHARACTER IN AN ANIMATED MOVIE? _____

11. Weirdest animal you've ever seen? _____

12. Fave clothing brand? ○ Nah ○ Yes, _____

13. ○ Cake ○ Cupcake? What kind?

_____

14. Fictional character you wish were real?

15. ○ STYLE OVER COMFORT ○ COMFORT OVER STYLE?

16. Fave beverage on ice?

_____

17. Tastiest frozen treat? _____

18. Better at speaking ○ to a crowd ○ one-on-one ○ to a group of friends?

19. What do your parents always bug you about? _____

_____

20. Dish you love to make?

coke or pepsi?

WHAT ARE YOUR
iNiTiALS?

1. FAVORITE
KiND OF DOG?

2. DO YOUR MOVIES NEED A HAPPY ENDING?
• NO • DEPENDS • ALWAYS

3. YOUR BEST PERSONALITY TRAIT?

4. YOUR NOT-SO-AWESOME PERSONALITY TRAIT?

5. WHO'S YOUR HERO?

6. ○ Love waking up to birds! ○ No, not the birds!

7. If you were a crayon, which color would you be?

8. What do you know a lot about? _____

9. What do you know nothing about? _____

10. ○ Board games ○ Bored with games?

11. Who taught you to tie your shoes? _____

12. MOST EMBARRASSING MOMENT EVER?

_____

13. Holidays with your family are ○ really fun ○ OK ○ kind of crazy?

14. FAVE THING YOU COULD GIVE UP FOR 1 YEAR?

_____

15. FAVE THING YOU COULD NOT GIVE UP FOR 1 YEAR?

_____

16. First thing you do in the morning?

_____

17. ○ Swiss cheese
○ Cheddar cheese
○ No cheese, please!

_____

18. Last thing you do before bed?

_____

19. WHAT WOULD YOU LOVE TO DO BUT THINK YOU CAN'T?

20. SPAGHETTI AND ○ MEATBALLS ○ CLAMS ○ OTHER _____ ?

coke or pepsi?

FIRST, MIDDLE, & LAST NAME

○ SMALL TOWN
○ BIG CITY
GOTTA FAVE?

WHICH IS WORSE?
○ BRUSSELS SPROUTS ○ BROCCOLI?

○ SWEET TASTING
○ TANGY FRO-YO?

COOLEST ADULT YOU KNOW?

FAVE SPUDS?
○ FRENCH FRIES ○ BAKED
○ HOME FRIES ○ CHIPS

HOW DO YOU LIKE SPICY FOOD?
○ MILD ○ MEDIUM ○ KABOOM!

FAVORITE
GRADE IN SCHOOL?

FOREIGN FILMS?
○ YES, FUN!
○ NO, SUBTITLES
ARE ANNOYING!

WHAT DO YOU THINK OF WHEN YOU HEAR THE WORD ORANGE?

WHAT DO YOU THINK OF WHEN YOU SEE THE WORD RED?

OPEN UMBRELLAS INDOORS?
○ YES ○ NO

EVER SNORT WHEN YOU LAUGH?
○ HA, YES!
○ NAH

EVER FALLEN DOWN IN PUBLIC?
○ YES
○ NO

○ SCRAMBLED
○ HARD BOILED
○ FRIED
○ NO EGGS?

EASIEST PERSON TO BUY A GIFT FOR?

MOST PEACEFUL COLOR?

WHICH IS WORSE?
○ NEVER BEING ABLE TO TEXT
○ NEVER BEING ABLE TO CALL

READ INSTRUCTIONS?
○ ALWAYS ○ SOMETIMES ○ NEVER!

WALK UNDER LADDERS?
○ NO WAY!
○ YEP

EVER FORGOTTEN TO REMOVE A PRICE TAG FROM YOUR CLOTHES?
○ yes ○ no

coke or pepsi?

NAME

1. WHAT'S YOUR RINGTONE?

2. MOST POPULAR COLOR iN YOUR CLOSET?

3. LAST THiNG YOU TOOK A PHOTO OF?

4. HOW DiD YOU MEET YOUR BFF?

5. BANANA • & P-NUT BUTTER
• NUT BREAD • CREAM PiE?

6. Ice skating is ⚪ so fun ⚪ OK ⚪ an accident waiting to happen?

7. Movie with the best ending? _____

8. Movie with the worst ending? _____

9. ⚪ Grilled ⚪ Roasted ⚪ Fried ⚪ Tofu chicken?

10. Fave TV actress? _____

11. Fave TV actor? _____

12. Fave song right now? _____

13. HARD FOR YOU TO SAY YOU'RE WRONG? ⚪ YES ⚪ WITH SOME PEOPLE ⚪ NOT REALLY

14. ⚪ Thick ⚪ Thin ⚪ Sicilian ⚪ Stuffed pizza?

15. Least favorite subject in school? _____

16. EVER GO THRU A "DO NOT ENTER" DOOR? ⚪ YES ⚪ NO

17. Are you usually too ⚪ hot ⚪ cold?

18. Allergic to anything? ⚪ No ⚪ Yes, _____

19. BEST-EVER SANDWICH? _____

20. Fashion trend you love right now?

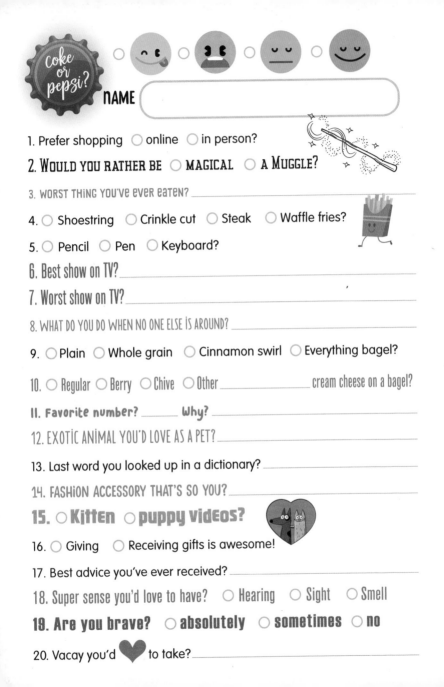

coke or pepsi?

NAME _____

1. Prefer shopping ○ online ○ in person?

2. WOULD YOU RATHER BE ○ MAGICAL ○ A MUGGLE?

3. WORST THING YOU'VE EVER EATEN? _____

4. ○ Shoestring ○ Crinkle cut ○ Steak ○ Waffle fries?

5. ○ Pencil ○ Pen ○ Keyboard?

6. Best show on TV? _____

7. Worst show on TV? _____

8. WHAT DO YOU DO WHEN NO ONE ELSE IS AROUND? _____

9. ○ Plain ○ Whole grain ○ Cinnamon swirl ○ Everything bagel?

10. ○ Regular ○ Berry ○ Chive ○ Other _____ cream cheese on a bagel?

11. Favorite number? _____ Why? _____

12. EXOTIC ANIMAL YOU'D LOVE AS A PET? _____

13. Last word you looked up in a dictionary? _____

14. FASHION ACCESSORY THAT'S SO YOU? _____

15. ○ Kitten ○ puppy videos?

16. ○ Giving ○ Receiving gifts is awesome!

17. Best advice you've ever received? _____

18. Super sense you'd love to have? ○ Hearing ○ Sight ○ Smell

19. Are you brave? ○ absolutely ○ sometimes ○ no

20. Vacay you'd ♥ to take? _____

movie you can watch over and over again?

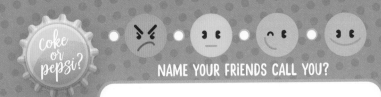

NAME YOUR FRIENDS CALL YOU?

1. SONG YOU GET STUCK iN YOUR HEAD?

2. IF YOU WERE A DJ, WHAT KiND OF MUSiC WOULD YOU PLAY?

3. FAVE WAY TO DiSCOVER NEW MUSiC?

4. SONG YOU ALWAYS GET UP AND DANCE TO?

5. SONG YOU CAN'T STAND?

6. Fave text abbreviation?

7. Least fave text abbreviation?

8. WEAR GREEN ON ST. PATRICK'S DAY?
○ ALWAYS   ○ SOMETIMES   ○ NEVER

9. One word to describe your BFF?

_____

10. WHAT'S MORE FUN?   ○ SLEEPOVER   ○ PARTY

11. DO YOU KNOW HOW TO YO-YO?
○ YES   ○ KIND OF   ○ NO

12. ○ Picnic in the park   ○ Fun night out?

13. Worst chore ever? _____

14. Watch anything last night? ○ No ○ Yes, _____

15. Playground game you miss? _____

16. Are you more ○ emotional   ○ logical   ○ 50/50?

17. WOULD YOU DESCRIBE YOURSELF AS ○ EXTROVERTED   ○ INTROVERTED   ○ IN THE MIDDLE?

18. How would your family describe you? _____

_____

19. CELEBRITY YOU'RE THE MOST LIKE? _____

20. If you could, what would you splurge on? _____

_____

coke or pepsi?

NAME

1. NAME YOU WISH YOU HAD?

2. ○ I'M THE QUEEN OF
   ○ ENOUGH WITH THE
   ○ OTHER _____
   SELFIES?

3. ○ MAC ○ PC?

4. IF YOUR PET COULD TALK, WHAT 3 QUESTIONS WOULD YOU ASK IT?

5. DOES YOUR PET HAVE A COOL TRICK OR SWEET HABIT?

CHECK OUT MY NEW SHADES!

6. CELEB YOU'D LOVE AS YOUR OTHER BFF? _____

7. Vacation ○ in the big city ○ warm beach ○ another country?

8. Family's favorite meal? _____

9. Waffles with ○ strawberries & whipped cream ○ butter & maple syrup?

10. Best thing on your bedroom walls? _____

11. Ever been a member of a fan club? ○ No ○ Yes, _____

12. DO YOU HAVE A CELEBRITY AUTOGRAPH? ○ NO ○ YES, _____

13. Favorite song to sing with friends?

14. ○ Fast food ○ Themed restaurant ○ Fine dining?

15. FAVE VEGGIE?

16. Do your friends love your
○ sense of humor
○ talent
○ style?

17. Poetry is
○ awesome
○ OK
○ so boring?

18. Tell people there's food stuck in their teeth?
○ Never ○ Depends ○ Always

19. Something you do really fast? _____

20. Is your dream machine a(n)
○ limo with driver ○ SUV
○ sports car ○ hybrid?

coke
or
pepsi?

NAME

WHO HAS IT EASIER?
- GIRLS
- BOYS
- ☞ WHY?

HOW MANY PAIRS OF SHOES DO YOU OWN?
- NOT ENOUGH
- JUST RIGHT
- TOO MANY!

SOMETHING YOU ♥ THAT MOST PEOPLE HATE?

WHAT'S YOUR BEST HABIT?

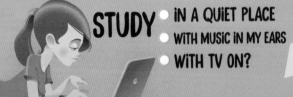

STUDY
- IN A QUIET PLACE
- WITH MUSIC IN MY EARS
- WITH TV ON?

HOW ARE YOU WHEN WAITING **IN LONG LINES?**

○ COOL ○ IRRITATED ○ I WALK AWAY!

FAVE SNEAKER COLOR?

○ ● ○ ● ○ ● ○ ● ○ ●

OTHER _____

EVER BEEN ON TV?
○ NOPE ○ YES,

TV SHOW THAT WOULD BE FUN TO ⭐ IN?

LAST SITCH WHICH REALLY UPSET YOU?

EVER BELIEVE A MONSTER WAS UNDER YOUR BED?
○ YES
○ NO

FAVE FREE-TIME THING TO DO?

LAST MOVIE YOU SAW?

FAVE JUNK FOOD?

FAVE SUPER HEALTHY FOOD?

MOST BORING BOOK YOU'VE EVER READ?

HARD TO SAY YOU'RE SORRY?
● YES
● SOMETIMES
● NO

GO-TO MOVIE FOOD?
○ POPCORN ○ TWIZZLERS
○ NACHOS ○ OTHER

coke or pepsi?

NAME [   ]

1. SOMETHING YOU'RE PROUD OF?

[   ]

2. CHOPSTICKS?
- ○ SO FUN!
- ○ SO ANNOYING!
- ○ FORK, PLEASE.

3. FICTIONAL PLACE YOU'D LOVE TO VISIT?

[   ]

4. WOULD YOU KISS A FROG IF YOU KNEW IT WOULD TURN INTO A HANDSOME PRINCE?
○ SURE! ○ NO WAY!

5. WHAT'S YOUR TYPICAL SUNDAY MORNING?

[   ]

6. Favorite craft to make? _____

7. SCARED OF HEIGHTS? ○ YES! ○ NO ○ DEPENDS HOW HIGH.

8. Scared of spiders? ○ Ahh! Yes! ○ Nope

9. __ Finding a leprechaun __ Finding his pot of gold?

10. ○ Chocolate cake with chocolate ganache ○ Angel food cake with berries?

11. Jewelry you always wear? _____

12. Word you always misspell? _____

13. What or who totally amazes you?

14. ○ Long road trip ○ Short flight to your destination?

15. WHICH IS MORE EXCITING? ○ GRAMMYS ○ OSCARS

16. Ever entered a competition? ○ No ○ Yes, _____

17. VACATION IN ○ THE USA ○ AN EXOTIC LOCATION?

18. What would be a fun business to start?

19. Chew gum? ○ No ○ Yes, I love

20. Who's your favorite superhero?

coke or pepsi?

NAME ON YOUR BIRTH CERTIFICATE?

1. **DAY, DATE & TIME YOU WERE BORN?**

2. **SOMETHING MOST PEOPLE DON'T KNOW ABOUT YOU?**

3. **WHAT DO YOU DO WHEN YOU'RE**  MAD?

• YELL • CRY • GET QUIET

4. **WHO DO YOU SPILL YOUR GUTS TO?**

5. • **MAKE QUICK DECISIONS**
   • **THINK ABOUT IT**
   • **AVOID DECISION-MAKING?**

6. ○ TACO ○ BURRITO ○ ENCHILADA ○ FAJITA?

SAUCE ME!

7. Which is worse? ○ Paper cut ○ Burning your tongue

8. LAST THING YOU WROTE ABOUT? _____

9. Are you a hat girl? ○ No ○ Yes, I own_____ hats.

10. **What would you do with an extra hour every day?**

11. What's a typical Saturday for you? _____

12. First word you said? _____

13. Weirdest thing in your backpack or bag?

14. ○ **Early** ○ **Right on time** ○ **Late to class?**

15. Best memory you have? _____

_____

16. What do you always lose? ○ socks ○ ponytail holders ○ pens

17. ○ Rays of sunshine on your face ○ Cool breeze in the shade?

18. *Language you'd like to learn?*

19. If you found $50, would you ○ save it ○ spend it ○ try to find its owner?

20. EVER FLOWN IN A HELICOPTER? ○ NO ○ YES, _____

ALL THE NAMES YOU GO BY?

ONE WORD TO
DESCRIBE YOURSELF?

THREE WORDS
TO DESCRIBE GIRLS?

1.

2.

3.

MOST MAGICAL?
- PEGASUS • UNICORN
- DRAGON • OTHER ↓

- ROCK STAR
- STARFISH
- SHOOTING STAR?

FAVORITE SONG FROM A MOVIE?

READ ANYTHING GOOD LATELY?
- NOT REALLY • OH YEAH, IT'S

- CHOCOLATE • PRETZELS
- CHOCOLATE-COVERED PRETZELS?

WHAT'S OUTSIDE THE WINDOW CLOSEST TO YOU?

CAN YOU WHISTLE A TUNE?

○ YES
○ A LITTLE BIT
○ NO

THREE WORDS TO DESCRIBE BOYS?

1.

2.

3.

WHAT KIND OF STUDENT ARE YOU?
○ GOOD ○ GREAT
○ COULD BE BETTER

○ MOUNTAIN CLIMBING
○ HIKING TRAILS
○ S'MORES AROUND A CAMPFIRE?

TRAMPOLINES?
○ YES, LOVE THEM!
○ NO WAY!

EVER BEEN PRANKED? ○ NO ○ YES,

WHO MAKES YOU LAUGH THE HARDEST?

WEIRDEST MOVIE YOU'VE SEEN?

SOMETHING YOU'RE OBSESSED WITH?

WHAT DRIVES YOU CRAZY?

WHAT MAKES YOU FEEL REALLY LOVED?

NAME

1. WHAT'S ON YOUR CALENDAR THIS WEEK?

2. LAST THING YOU COOKED, MICROWAVED, OR TOASTED?

3. FAVORITE
ROOM IN YOUR HOME?

4. HOW DO YOU LIKE TO
DECORATE?

5. WHAT'S YOUR FASHION STYLE?

6. EVER WEAR YOUR FRIENDS' CLOTHES? ○ NOT REALLY ○ ⊙ OH YEAH

7. SPRINKLES & GLITTER
 ○ MAKE EVERYTHING FUN ○ ARE ANNOYING & MESSY?

8. Who encourages you the most? _____

9. Staying organized ○ is so helpful ○ messes up creativity?

10. Something you wish you were good at? _____

_____

11. SOMETHING NEW YOU'VE LEARNED? _____

12. Favorite holiday treat? _____

13. Eggnog? ○ Love it! ○ So gross!

14. Celebrity wardrobe you'd love to borrow from?

_____

15. Are you squeamish? ○ Totally ○ Nah

16. ARE YOU AN ADVENTUROUS EATER? ○ YES ○ NO

17. CAMPING STYLE? ○ TENT ○ CABIN ○ RV

18. Ever encountered a wild animal?

○ No ○ Yes, _____

19. Favorite amusement park?

_____

20. Are you having a
○ good ○ bad ○ horrible hair day?

coke or pepsi?

NAME YOU WRITE ON NAMETAG?

○ ○ ○ ?

1. WHAT WOULD YOU DO WITH $1,000 IN ONE DAY?

2. DO YOU LIKE BEING IN THE SPOTLIGHT?
○ YES
○ NO

3. WHAT MAKES YOU LOSE TRACK OF TIME?

4. ○ SOUR CREAM ○ BARBEQUE ○ CHEDDAR ○ OTHER CHIPS?

5. WHAT DO YOU DO IN YOUR SPARE TIME?

MR. MEOW, WHAT SHOULD I WEAR TO THE DANCE?

6. DO YOU TALK TO YOUR PET LIKE IT'S A PERSON? ○ OF COURSE! ○ NAH

7. DO FRIENDS COUNT ON YOU FOR ○ PEP TALKS ○ REALITY CHECKS ○ SOME LAUGHS?

8. Fave game of all time? _____

9. **Best band ever?** _____

10. Favorite book character? _____

11. **How many times do you hit Snooze in the morning?** _____

12. FOOD YOU LOVE TO SMELL COOKING? _____

13. Where are you right now? _____

14. Where would you rather be? _____

15. Do you ○ think about the past ○ dream about the future more?

16. Have you ever been lost in a corn maze? ○ No ○ Yes!

17. Rather have a friend who ○ totally gets you ○ is tons of fun?

18. WHO DO YOU LOOK UP TO?

19. Ever fallen asleep in the middle of something? ○ No ○ Yes,

_____

20. **Chocolate &** ○ peanut butter ○ marshmallows ○ coconut?

Coke or pepsi?

MY NAME iS

I WiSH MY NAME WERE

LiTTLE KiDS ARE
○ FUN
○ ANNOYiNG?

FAMOUS PERSON YOU WOULD TRADE PLACES WiTH?

WHAT'S BETTER?
○ ASKiNG QUESTIONS
○ GiViNG ANSWERS

FAMOUS PERSON YOU'D NEVER TRADE PLACES WiTH?

EVER BEEN EMBARRASSED BY YOUR PARENTS?
● NO ● YES

SMARTEST PERSON YOU KNOW?

● COMFY
● TRENDY
SHOES?

IF YOU COULD INVENT SOMETHING, WHAT WOULD IT BE?

RULES SHOULD BE
○ FOLLOWED ○ USED AS GUIDELINES ○ BROKEN?

WORST FASHION MISTAKE YOU'VE EVER MADE?

○ PAY NOW PLAY LATER
○ PLAY NOW PAY LATER?

. . . .

STUDY
○ ALONE
○ WITH A FRIEND
○ IN A GROUP?

BEST THING ABOUT SCHOOL?

MOST ANNOYING THING ABOUT SCHOOL?

MOST OUTRAGEOUS THING YOU'VE EVER EATEN?

WRITE papers
● IN ADVANCE
● THE NIGHT BEFORE?

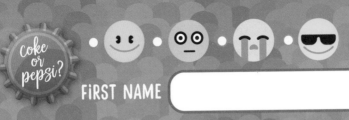

coke or pepsi?

FIRST NAME

1. STORY BEHIND YOUR FIRST NAME? • NO • YES

2. IF YOU COULD GO TO ONLY ONE CONCERT THIS YEAR, WHICH WOULD IT BE?

3. • PAY ATTENTION TO LYRICS
• JUST ROCK OUT TO THE MUSIC
• BOTH?

4. HOW WOULD YOUR FRIENDS DESCRIBE YOU?
• SWEET • RELIABLE • A LITTLE CRAY-CRAY?

5. EVER BEEN IN A PLAY? • NO • YES

6. Are you good at telling jokes? ○ Yes ○ No

7. Which would be fun to play? ○ Damsel in distress ○ Spy ○ Supervillain

8. Biggest question about life? _____

9. Have a fave cartoon? ○ Nope ○ Yep, _____

10. BEST CHARACTER iN AN ANiMATED MOViE? _____

11. Weirdest animal you've ever seen? _____

12. Fave clothing brand? ○ Nah ○ Yes, _____

13. ○ Cake ○ Cupcake? What kind?

_____

14. Fictional character you wish were real?

15. ○ STYLE OVER COMFORT ○ COMFORT OVER STYLE?

16. Fave beverage on ice?

_____

17. Tastiest frozen treat? _____

18. Better at speaking ○ to a crowd ○ one-on-one ○ to a group of friends?

19. What do your parents always bug you about? _____

_____

20. Dish you love to make?

coke or pepsi?

WHAT ARE YOUR **INITIALS?**

1. FAVORITE KIND OF DOG?

2. DO YOUR MOVIES NEED A HAPPY ENDING?
• NO • DEPENDS • ALWAYS

3. YOUR BEST PERSONALITY TRAIT?

4. YOUR NOT-SO-AWESOME PERSONALITY TRAIT?

5. WHO'S YOUR HERO?

6. ⭘ Love waking up to birds! ⭘ No, not the birds!

7. If you were a crayon, which color would you be?

8. What do you know a lot about? _____

9. What do you know nothing about? _____

10. ⭘ Board games ⭘ Bored with games?

11. Who taught you to tie your shoes? _____

12. MOST EMBARRASSING MOMENT EVER?

13. Holidays with your family are ⭘ really fun ⭘ OK ⭘ kind of crazy?

14. FAVE THING YOU COULD GIVE UP FOR 1 YEAR?

15. FAVE THING YOU COULD NOT GIVE UP FOR 1 YEAR?

16. First thing you do in the morning?

17. ⭘ Swiss cheese
    ⭘ Cheddar cheese
    ⭘ No cheese, please!

18. Last thing you do before bed?

19. WHAT WOULD YOU LOVE TO DO BUT THINK YOU CAN'T?

20. SPAGHETTI AND ⭘ MEATBALLS ⭘ CLAMS ⭘ OTHER _____ ?

coke or pepsi?

FIRST, MIDDLE, & LAST NAME

[ ]

○ SMALL TOWN
○ BIG CITY

WHICH IS WORSE?

GOTTA FAVE? ↘ ○ BRUSSELS SPROUTS ○ BROCCOLI?

[ ]

○ **SWEET TASTING**
○ **TANGY FRO-YO?**

COOLEST ADULT YOU KNOW?

[ ]

FAVE SPUDS?

○ FRENCH FRIES   ○ BAKED
○ HOME FRIES   ○ CHIPS

HOW DO YOU LIKE SPICY FOOD?
○ MILD   ○ MEDIUM   ○ KABOOM!

FAVORITE GRADE IN SCHOOL?

FOREIGN FILMS?

○ YES, FUN!
○ NO, SUBTITLES
ARE ANNOYING!

WHAT DO YOU THINK OF WHEN YOU HEAR THE WORD ORANGE?

WHAT DO YOU THINK OF WHEN YOU SEE THE WORD RED?

OPEN UMBRELLAS INDOORS?
- YES
- NO

EVER SNORT WHEN YOU LAUGH?
- HA, YES!
- NAH

EVER FALLEN DOWN IN PUBLIC?
- YES
- NO

- SCRAMBLED
- HARD BOILED
- FRIED
- NO EGGS?

EASIEST PERSON TO BUY A GIFT FOR?

MOST PEACEFUL COLOR?

WHICH IS WORSE?
- NEVER BEING ABLE TO TEXT
- NEVER BEING ABLE TO CALL

READ INSTRUCTIONS?
- ALWAYS ○ SOMETIMES ○ NEVER!

WALK UNDER LADDERS?
- NO WAY!
- YEP

EVER FORGOTTEN TO REMOVE A PRICE TAG FROM YOUR CLOTHES?
- yes
- no

coke or pepsi?

NAME

1. WHAT'S YOUR RINGTONE?

2. MOST POPULAR COLOR iN YOUR CLOSET?

3. LAST THING YOU TOOK A PHOTO OF?

4. HOW DiD YOU MEET YOUR BFF?

5. BANANA • & P-NUT BUTTER
• NUT BREAD • CREAM PiE?

6. Ice skating is ◯ so fun ◯ OK ◯ an accident waiting to happen?

7. Movie with the best ending? _____

8. Movie with the worst ending? _____

9. ◯ Grilled ◯ Roasted ◯ Fried ◯ Tofu chicken?

10. Fave TV actress? _____

11. Fave TV actor? _____

12. Fave song right now?

13. HARD FOR YOU TO SAY YOU'RE WRONG? ◯ YES ◯ WITH SOME PEOPLE ◯ NOT REALLY

14. ◯ Thick ◯ Thin ◯ Sicilian ◯ Stuffed pizza?

15. Least favorite subject in school? _____

16. EVER GO THRU A "DO NOT ENTER" DOOR? ◯ YES ◯ NO

17. Are you usually too ◯ hot ◯ cold?

18. Allergic to anything? ◯ No ◯ Yes, _____

19. BEST-EVER SANDWICH? _____

20. Fashion trend you love right now?

coke or pepsi?

NAME

1. Prefer shopping ○ online ○ in person?

2. WOULD YOU RATHER BE ○ MAGICAL ○ A MUGGLE?

3. WORST THING YOU'VE EVER EATEN? _____

4. ○ Shoestring ○ Crinkle cut ○ Steak ○ Waffle fries?

5. ○ Pencil ○ Pen ○ Keyboard?

6. Best show on TV? _____

7. Worst show on TV? _____

8. WHAT DO YOU DO WHEN NO ONE ELSE IS AROUND? _____

9. ○ Plain ○ Whole grain ○ Cinnamon swirl ○ Everything bagel?

10. ○ Regular ○ Berry ○ Chive ○ Other _____ cream cheese on a bagel?

11. Favorite number? _____ Why? _____

12. EXOTIC ANIMAL YOU'D LOVE AS A PET? _____

13. Last word you looked up in a dictionary? _____

14. FASHION ACCESSORY THAT'S SO YOU? _____

15. ○ Kitten ○ puppy videos?

16. ○ Giving ○ Receiving gifts is awesome!

17. Best advice you've ever received? _____

18. Super sense you'd love to have? ○ Hearing ○ Sight ○ Smell

19. Are you brave? ○ absolutely ○ sometimes ○ no

20. Vacay you'd ♥ to take? _____

movie you can watch over and over again?

NAME YOUR FRIENDS CALL YOU?

1. SONG YOU GET STUCK IN YOUR HEAD?

2. IF YOU WERE A DJ, WHAT KIND OF MUSIC WOULD YOU PLAY?

3. FAVE WAY TO DISCOVER NEW MUSIC?

4. SONG YOU ALWAYS GET UP AND DANCE TO?

5. SONG YOU CAN'T STAND?

6. Fave text abbreviation?

7. Least fave text abbreviation?

8. WEAR GREEN ON ST. PATRICK'S DAY?
○ ALWAYS ○ SOMETIMES ○ NEVER

9. One word to describe your BFF?
_____

10. WHAT'S MORE FUN? ○ SLEEPOVER ○ PARTY

11. DO YOU KNOW HOW TO YO-YO?
○ YES ○ KIND OF ○ NO

12. ○ Picnic in the park ○ Fun night out?

13. Worst chore ever? _____

14. Watch anything last night? ○ No ○ Yes, _____

15. Playground game you miss? _____

16. Are you more ○ emotional ○ logical ○ 50/50?

17. WOULD YOU DESCRIBE YOURSELF AS ○ EXTROVERTED ○ INTROVERTED ○ IN THE MIDDLE?

18. How would your family describe you? _____
_____

19. CELEBRITY YOU'RE THE MOST LIKE? _____

20. If you could, what would you splurge on? _____
_____

coke or pepsi?

NAME

1. NAME YOU WISH YOU HAD?

2. ○ I'M THE QUEEN OF
   ○ ENOUGH WITH THE
   ○ OTHER _____
   SELFIES?

3. ○ MAC ○ PC?

CHECK OUT MY NEW SHADES!

4. IF YOUR PET COULD TALK, WHAT 3 QUESTIONS WOULD YOU ASK IT?

5. DOES YOUR PET HAVE A COOL TRICK OR SWEET HABIT?

6. CELEB YOU'D LOVE AS YOUR OTHER BFF? _____

7. Vacation ○ in the big city ○ warm beach ○ another country?

8. Family's favorite meal? _____

9. Waffles with ○ strawberries & whipped cream ○ butter & maple syrup?

10. Best thing on your bedroom walls? _____

11. Ever been a member of a fan club? ○ No ○ Yes, _____

12. DO YOU HAVE A CELEBRITY AUTOGRAPH? ○ NO ○ YES, _____

13. Favorite song to sing with friends? (   )

14. ○ Fast food ○ Themed restaurant ○ Fine dining?

15. FAVE VEGGIE? (   )

16. Do your friends love your
    ○ sense of humor
    ○ talent
    ○ style?

17. Poetry is
    ○ awesome
    ○ OK
    ○ so boring?

18. Tell people there's food stuck in their teeth?
    ○ Never ○ Depends ○ Always

19. Something you do really fast? _____

20. Is your dream machine a(n)
    ○ limo with driver ○ SUV
    ○ sports car ○ hybrid?

 coke or pepsi?

NAME

WHO HAS iT EASiER?
- GiRLS
- BOYS
- ☞WHY?

HOW MANY PAiRS OF SHOES DO YOU OWN?
- NOT ENOUGH - JUST RiGHT - TOO MANY!

SOMETHiNG YOU ♥ THAT MOST PEOPLE HATE?

WHAT'S YOUR BEST HABiT?

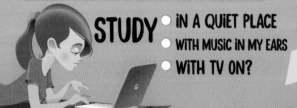 STUDY
- iN A QUIET PLACE
- WiTH MUSiC iN MY EARS
- WiTH TV ON?

HOW ARE YOU WHEN WAITING iN LONG LiNES?

○ COOL ○ iRRITATED ○ I WALK AWAY!

FAVE SNEAKER COLOR?

○ ● ○ ● ○ ● ○ ● ○ ●

OTHER _____

EVER BEEN ON TV?
○ NOPE ○ YES,

TV SHOW THAT WOULD BE FUN TO ★ iN?

LAST SiTCH WHiCH REALLY UPSET YOU?

_____

EVER BELIEVE A MONSTER WAS UNDER YOUR BED?
○ YES
○ NO

FAVE FREE-TiME THiNG TO DO?

_____

LAST MOVIE YOU SAW?

FAVE JUNK FOOD?

_____

FAVE SUPER HEALTHY FOOD?

_____

MOST BORiNG BOOK YOU'VE EVER READ?

HARD TO SAY YOU'RE SORRY?
● YES
● SOMETiMES
● NO

GO-TO MOVIE FOOD?
○ POPCORN ○ TWiZZLERS
○ NACHOS ○ OTHER

_____

coke or pepsi?

NAME

1. SOMETHING YOU'RE PROUD OF?

2. CHOPSTICKS?
○ SO FUN!
○ SO ANNOYING!
3. FICTIONAL PLACE ○ FORK, PLEASE.
YOU'D LOVE TO VISIT?

4. WOULD YOU KISS A FROG IF YOU KNEW IT WOULD TURN INTO A HANDSOME PRINCE?
○ SURE! ○ NO WAY!

5. WHAT'S YOUR TYPICAL SUNDAY MORNING?

6. Favorite craft to make? _____

7. SCARED OF HEIGHTS? ○ YES! ○ NO ○ DEPENDS HOW HIGH.

8. Scared of spiders? ○ Ahh! Yes! ○ Nope

9. __ Finding a leprechaun __ Finding his pot of gold?

10. ○ Chocolate cake with chocolate ganache ○ Angel food cake with berries?

11. Jewelry you always wear? _____

12. Word you always misspell? _____

13. What or who totally amazes you?

14. ○ Long road trip ○ Short flight to your destination?

15. WHICH IS MORE EXCITING? ○ GRAMMYS ○ OSCARS

16. Ever entered a competition? ○ No ○ Yes, _____

17. VACATION IN ○ THE USA ○ AN EXOTIC LOCATION?

18. What would be a fun business to start?

19. Chew gum? ○ No ○ Yes, I love

20. Who's your favorite superhero?

coke or pepsi?

NAME ON YOUR BIRTH CERTIFICATE?

1. DAY, DATE & TIME YOU WERE BORN?

2. SOMETHING MOST PEOPLE DON'T KNOW ABOUT YOU?

3. WHAT DO YOU DO WHEN YOU'RE

MAD?

● YELL ● CRY ● GET QUIET

4. WHO DO YOU SPILL YOUR GUTS TO?

5. ● MAKE QUICK DECISIONS
● THINK ABOUT IT
● AVOID DECISION-MAKING?

6. ○ TACO ○ BURRITO ○ ENCHILADA ○ FAJITA?

SAUCE ME!

7. Which is worse? ○ Paper cut ○ Burning your tongue

8. LAST THING YOU WROTE ABOUT? _____

9. Are you a hat girl? ○ No ○ Yes, I own _____ hats.

10. What would you do with an extra hour every day?

11. What's a typical Saturday for you? _____

12. First word you said? _____

13. Weirdest thing in your backpack or bag?

14. ○ Early ○ Right on time ○ Late to class?

15. Best memory you have? _____

_____

16. What do you always lose? ○ socks ○ ponytail holders ○ pens

17. ○ Rays of sunshine on your face ○ Cool breeze in the shade?

18. Language you'd like to learn?

19. If you found $50, would you ○ save it ○ spend it ○ try to find its owner?

20. EVER FLOWN IN A HELICOPTER? ○ NO ○ YES, _____

coke or pepsi?

ALL THE NAMES YOU GO BY?

ONE WORD TO DESCRIBE YOURSELF?

THREE WORDS TO DESCRIBE GIRLS?

1.

2.

3.

MOST MAGICAL?
- PEGASUS - UNICORN
- DRAGON - OTHER ↓

- ROCK STAR
- STARFISH
- SHOOTING STAR?

FAVORITE SONG FROM A MOVIE?

READ ANYTHING GOOD LATELY?
- NOT REALLY - OH YEAH, IT'S

- CHOCOLATE - PRETZELS
- CHOCOLATE-COVERED PRETZELS?

WHAT'S OUTSIDE THE WINDOW CLOSEST TO YOU?

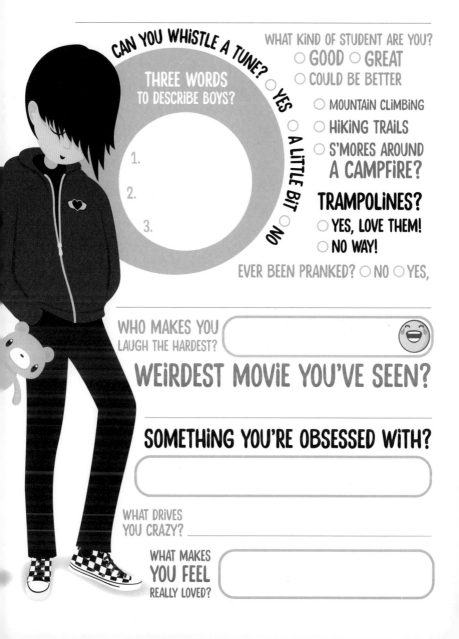

CAN YOU WHISTLE A TUNE?

○ YES

○ A LITTLE BIT

○ NO

THREE WORDS TO DESCRIBE BOYS?

1.

2.

3.

WHAT KIND OF STUDENT ARE YOU?
○ GOOD ○ GREAT
○ COULD BE BETTER

○ MOUNTAIN CLIMBING
○ HIKING TRAILS
○ S'MORES AROUND A CAMPFIRE?

TRAMPOLINES?
○ YES, LOVE THEM!
○ NO WAY!

EVER BEEN PRANKED? ○ NO ○ YES,

WHO MAKES YOU LAUGH THE HARDEST?

WEIRDEST MOVIE YOU'VE SEEN?

SOMETHING YOU'RE OBSESSED WITH?

WHAT DRIVES YOU CRAZY?

WHAT MAKES **YOU FEEL** REALLY LOVED?

NAME

1. WHAT'S ON YOUR CALENDAR THIS WEEK?

2. LAST THING YOU COOKED, MICROWAVED, OR TOASTED?

3. FAVORITE
ROOM IN YOUR HOME?

4. HOW DO YOU LIKE TO
DECORATE?

5. WHAT'S YOUR FASHION STYLE?

6. EVER WEAR YOUR FRIENDS' CLOTHES? ○ NOT REALLY ○ ⊙ OH YEAH

7. SPRINKLES & GLITTER
   ○ MAKE EVERYTHING FUN ○ ARE ANNOYING & MESSY?

8. Who encourages you the most? _____

9. Staying organized ○ is so helpful ○ messes up creativity?

10. Something you wish you were good at? _____
_____

11. SOMETHING NEW YOU'VE LEARNED? _____

12. Favorite holiday treat? _____

13. Eggnog? ○ Love it! ○ So gross!

14. Celebrity wardrobe you'd love to borrow from?
_____

15. Are you squeamish? ○ Totally ○ Nah

16. ARE YOU AN ADVENTUROUS EATER? ○ YES ○ NO

17. CAMPING STYLE? ○ TENT ○ CABIN ○ RV

18. Ever encountered a wild animal?

○ No ○ Yes, _____

19. Favorite amusement park?

_____

20. Are you having a
○ good ○ bad ○ horrible hair day?

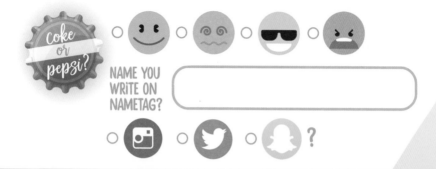

coke or pepsi?

NAME YOU
WRITE ON
NAMETAG?

?

1. WHAT WOULD YOU DO WITH $1,000 IN ONE DAY?

2. DO YOU LIKE BEING IN THE SPOTLIGHT?
○ YES
○ NO

3. WHAT MAKES YOU LOSE TRACK OF TIME?

4.
○ SOUR CREAM ○ BARBEQUE ○ CHEDDAR
○ OTHER CHIPS?

5. WHAT DO YOU DO IN YOUR SPARE TIME?

MR. MEOW, WHAT SHOULD I WEAR TO THE DANCE?

6. DO YOU TALK TO YOUR PET LIKE IT'S A PERSON? ○ OF COURSE! ○ NAH

7. DO FRIENDS COUNT ON YOU FOR ○ PEP TALKS ○ REALITY CHECKS ○ SOME LAUGHS?

8. Fave game of all time? _____

9. Best band ever? _____

10. Favorite book character? _____

11. How many times do you hit Snooze in the morning? _____

12. FOOD YOU LOVE TO SMELL COOKING? _____

13. Where are you right now? _____

14. Where would you rather be? _____

15. Do you ○ think about the past ○ dream about the future more?

16. Have you ever been lost in a corn maze? ○ No ○ Yes!

17. Rather have a friend who ○ totally gets you ○ is tons of fun?

18. WHO DO YOU LOOK UP TO?

19. Ever fallen asleep in the middle of something? ○ No ○ Yes,

_____

20. Chocolate & ○ peanut butter ○ marshmallows ○ coconut?

coke or pepsi?

MY
name is

I WISH MY NAME WERE

LITTLE KIDS ARE
○ FUN
○ ANNOYING?

FAMOUS PERSON YOU WOULD TRADE PLACES WITH?

WHAT'S BETTER?
○ ASKING QUESTIONS
○ GIVING ANSWERS

FAMOUS PERSON YOU'D NEVER TRADE PLACES WITH?

EVER BEEN EMBARRASSED BY YOUR PARENTS?
● NO ● YES
☞

SMARTEST PERSON YOU KNOW?

● COMFY
● TRENDY
SHOES?

 IF YOU COULD INVENT SOMETHING, WHAT WOULD IT BE?

RULES SHOULD BE
○ FOLLOWED ○ USED AS GUIDELINES ○ BROKEN?

WORST FASHION MISTAKE YOU'VE EVER MADE?
○ PAY NOW PLAY LATER
○ PLAY NOW PAY LATER?

STUDY
○ ALONE
○ WITH A FRIEND
○ IN A GROUP?

BEST THING ABOUT SCHOOL?

MOST ANNOYING THING ABOUT SCHOOL?

MOST OUTRAGEOUS THING YOU'VE EVER EATEN?

WRITE papers
• IN ADVANCE
• THE NIGHT BEFORE?

FIRST NAME

1. STORY BEHIND YOUR FIRST NAME? ● NO ● YES

2. IF YOU COULD GO TO ONLY ONE CONCERT THIS YEAR, WHICH WOULD IT BE?

3. ● PAY ATTENTION TO LYRICS
● JUST ROCK OUT TO THE MUSIC
● BOTH?

4. HOW WOULD YOUR FRIENDS DESCRIBE YOU?
● SWEET ● RELIABLE ● A LITTLE CRAY-CRAY?

5. EVER BEEN IN A PLAY? ● NO ● YES

6. Are you good at telling jokes? ○ Yes ○ No

7. Which would be fun to play? ○ Damsel in distress ○ Spy ○ Supervillain

8. Biggest question about life? _____

9. Have a fave cartoon? ○ Nope ○ Yep. _____

10. BEST CHARACTER IN AN ANIMATED MOVIE? _____

11. Weirdest animal you've ever seen? _____

12. Fave clothing brand? ○ Nah ○ Yes, _____

13. ○ Cake ○ Cupcake? What kind?

_____

14. Fictional character you wish were real?

15. ○ STYLE OVER COMFORT ○ COMFORT OVER STYLE?

16. Fave beverage on ice?

_____

17. Tastiest frozen treat? _____

18. Better at speaking ○ to a crowd ○ one-on-one ○ to a group of friends?

19. What do your parents always bug you about? _____

_____

20. Dish you love to make?

coke or pepsi?

WHAT ARE YOUR **INITIALS?**

1. FAVORITE KIND OF DOG?

2. DO YOUR MOVIES NEED A HAPPY ENDING?
• NO • DEPENDS • ALWAYS

3. YOUR BEST PERSONALITY TRAIT?

4. YOUR NOT-SO-AWESOME PERSONALITY TRAIT?

5. WHO'S YOUR HERO?

6. ○ Love waking up to birds! ○ No, not the birds!

7. If you were a crayon, which color would you be?

8. What do you know a lot about? _____

9. What do you know nothing about? _____

10. ○ Board games ○ Bored with games?

11. Who taught you to tie your shoes? _____

12. MOST EMBARRASSING MOMENT EVER?

_____

13. Holidays with your family are ○ really fun ○ OK ○ kind of crazy?

14. FAVE THING YOU COULD GIVE UP FOR 1 YEAR?

_____

15. FAVE THING YOU COULD NOT GIVE UP FOR 1 YEAR?

_____

16. First thing you do in the morning?

_____

17. ○ Swiss cheese
    ○ Cheddar cheese
    ○ No cheese, please!

18. Last thing you do before bed?

_____

19. WHAT WOULD YOU LOVE TO DO BUT THINK YOU CAN'T?

20. SPAGHETTI AND ○ MEATBALLS ○ CLAMS ○ OTHER _____ ?

FIRST, MIDDLE, & LAST NAME

○ SMALL TOWN
○ BIG CITY
GOTTA FAVE?

WHICH IS WORSE?
○ BRUSSELS SPROUTS ○ BROCCOLI?

○ SWEET TASTING
○ TANGY FRO-YO?

COOLEST ADULT YOU KNOW?

FAVE SPUDS?
○ FRENCH FRIES ○ BAKED
○ HOME FRIES ○ CHIPS

HOW DO YOU LIKE SPICY FOOD?
○ MILD ○ MEDIUM ○ KABOOM!

FAVORITE GRADE IN SCHOOL?

FOREIGN FILMS?
○ YES, FUN!
○ NO, SUBTITLES
ARE ANNOYING!

coke or pepsi?

NAME

1. WHAT'S YOUR RINGTONE?

2. MOST POPULAR COLOR IN YOUR CLOSET?

3. LAST THING YOU TOOK A PHOTO OF?

4. HOW DID YOU MEET YOUR BFF?

5. BANANA ● & P-NUT BUTTER
● NUT BREAD ● CREAM PIE?

6. Ice skating is ○ so fun ○ OK ○ an accident waiting to happen?

7. Movie with the best ending? _____

8. Movie with the worst ending? _____

9. ○ Grilled ○ Roasted ○ Fried ○ Tofu chicken?

10. Fave TV actress? _____

11. Fave TV actor? _____

12. Fave song right now?

13. HARD FOR YOU TO SAY YOU'RE WRONG? ○ YES ○ WITH SOME PEOPLE ○ NOT REALLY

14. ○ Thick ○ Thin ○ Sicilian ○ Stuffed pizza?

15. Least favorite subject in school? _____

16. EVER GO THRU A "DO NOT ENTER" DOOR? ○ YES ○ NO

17. Are you usually too ○ hot ○ cold?

18. Allergic to anything? ○ No ○ Yes, _____

19. BEST-EVER SANDWICH? _____

20. Fashion trend you love right now?

NAME [ ]

1. Prefer shopping ○ online ○ in person?
2. WOULD YOU RATHER BE ○ MAGICAL ○ A MUGGLE?
3. WORST THING YOU'VE EVER EATEN? _____
4. ○ Shoestring ○ Crinkle cut ○ Steak ○ Waffle fries?
5. ○ Pencil ○ Pen ○ Keyboard?
6. Best show on TV? _____
7. Worst show on TV? _____
8. WHAT DO YOU DO WHEN NO ONE ELSE IS AROUND? _____
9. ○ Plain ○ Whole grain ○ Cinnamon swirl ○ Everything bagel?
10. ○ Regular ○ Berry ○ Chive ○ Other _____ cream cheese on a bagel?
11. Favorite number? _____ Why? _____
12. EXOTIC ANIMAL YOU'D LOVE AS A PET? _____
13. Last word you looked up in a dictionary? _____
14. FASHION ACCESSORY THAT'S SO YOU? _____
15. ○ Kitten ○ puppy videos?
16. ○ Giving ○ Receiving gifts is awesome!
17. Best advice you've ever received? _____
18. Super sense you'd love to have? ○ Hearing ○ Sight ○ Smell
19. Are you brave? ○ absolutely ○ sometimes ○ no
20. Vacay you'd ♥ to take? _____

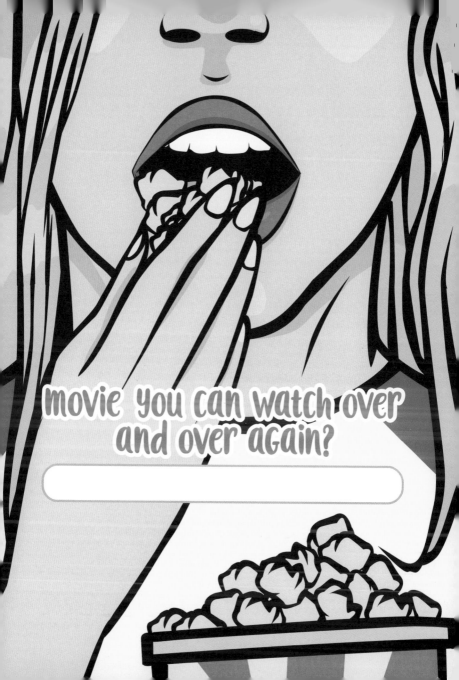

coke or pepsi?

NAME YOUR FRIENDS CALL YOU?

1. SONG YOU GET STUCK iN YOUR HEAD?

2. IF YOU WERE A DJ, WHAT KiND OF MUSiC WOULD YOU PLAY?

3. FAVE WAY TO DiSCOVER NEW MUSiC?

4. SONG YOU ALWAYS GET UP AND DANCE TO?

5. SONG YOU CAN'T STAND?

6. Fave text abbreviation?

7. Least fave text abbreviation?

8. WEAR GREEN ON ST. PATRICK'S DAY?
○ ALWAYS ○ SOMETIMES ○ NEVER

9. One word to describe your BFF?

_____

10. WHAT'S MORE FUN? ○ SLEEPOVER ○ PARTY

11. DO YOU KNOW HOW TO YO-YO?
○ YES   ○ KIND OF   ○ NO

12. ○ Picnic in the park   ○ Fun night out?

13. Worst chore ever? _____

14. Watch anything last night? ○ No ○ Yes, _____

15. Playground game you miss? _____

16. Are you more ○ emotional   ○ logical   ○ 50/50?

17. WOULD YOU DESCRIBE YOURSELF AS ○ EXTROVERTED   ○ INTROVERTED   ○ IN THE MIDDLE?

18. How would your family describe you? _____

_____

19. CELEBRITY YOU'RE THE MOST LIKE? _____

20. If you could, what would you splurge on? _____

_____

coke or pepsi?

NAME

1. **NAME YOU** WISH YOU HAD?

2. ○ I'M THE QUEEN OF
   ○ ENOUGH WITH THE
   ○ OTHER _____
   SELFIES?

3. ○ MAC ○ PC?

4. **IF YOUR PET COULD TALK, WHAT 3 QUESTIONS WOULD YOU ASK IT?**

CHECK OUT MY NEW SHADES!

5. DOES YOUR PET HAVE A COOL TRICK OR SWEET HABIT?

6. CELEB YOU'D LOVE AS YOUR OTHER BFF? _____

7. Vacation ○ in the big city ○ warm beach ○ another country?

8. Family's favorite meal? _____

9. Waffles with ○ strawberries & whipped cream ○ butter & maple syrup?

10. Best thing on your bedroom walls? _____

11. Ever been a member of a fan club? ○ No ○ Yes, _____

12. DO YOU HAVE A CELEBRITY AUTOGRAPH? ○ NO ○ YES, _____

13. Favorite song to sing with friends? ( )

14. ○ Fast food ○ Themed restaurant ○ Fine dining?

15. FAVE VEGGIE? ( )

16. Do your friends love your
○ sense of humor
○ talent
○ style?

17. Poetry is
○ awesome
○ OK
○ so boring?

18. Tell people there's food stuck in their teeth?
○ Never ○ Depends ○ Always

19. Something you do really fast? _____

20. Is your dream machine a(n)
○ limo with driver ○ SUV
○ sports car ○ hybrid?

coke or pepsi?

NAME

WHO HAS IT EASIER?
- GIRLS
- BOYS
- ☞WHY?

HOW MANY PAIRS OF SHOES DO YOU OWN?
- NOT ENOUGH
- JUST RIGHT
- TOO MANY!

SOMETHING YOU ♥ THAT MOST PEOPLE HATE?

WHAT'S YOUR BEST HABIT?

STUDY
- IN A QUIET PLACE
- WITH MUSIC IN MY EARS
- WITH TV ON?

HOW ARE YOU WHEN WAITING iN LONG LiNES?

○ COOL ○ iRRITATED ○ I WALK AWAY!

EVER BEEN ON TV?
○ NOPE ○ YES,

FAVE SNEAKER COLOR?

○ ● ○ ● ○ ● ○ ● ○ ●

OTHER _____

TV SHOW THAT WOULD BE FUN TO ⭐ iN?

LAST SiTCH WHICH REALLY UPSET YOU?

EVER BELIEVE A MONSTER WAS UNDER YOUR BED?
○ YES
○ NO

FAVE FREE-TIME THiNG TO DO?

LAST MOVIE YOU SAW?

FAVE JUNK FOOD?

FAVE SUPER HEALTHY FOOD?

HARD TO SAY YOU'RE SORRY?
● YES
● SOMETiMES
● NO

MOST BORiNG BOOK YOU'VE EVER READ?

GO-TO MOVIE FOOD?
○ POPCORN ○ TWIZZLERS
○ NACHOS ○ OTHER

coke or pepsi?

NAME

1. SOMETHING YOU'RE PROUD OF?

2. CHOPSTICKS?
○ SO FUN!
○ SO ANNOYING!
○ FORK, PLEASE.

3. FICTIONAL PLACE YOU'D LOVE TO VISIT?

4. WOULD YOU KISS A FROG IF YOU KNEW IT WOULD TURN INTO A HANDSOME PRINCE?
○ SURE! ○ NO WAY!

5. WHAT'S YOUR TYPICAL SUNDAY MORNING?

6. Favorite craft to make? _____

7. SCARED OF HEIGHTS? ○ YES! ○ NO ○ DEPENDS HOW HIGH.

8. Scared of spiders? ○ Ahh! Yes! ○ Nope

9. __ Finding a leprechaun __ Finding his pot of gold?

10. ○ Chocolate cake with chocolate ganache ○ Angel food cake with berries?

11. Jewelry you always wear? _____

12. Word you always misspell? _____

13. What or who totally amazes you?

14. ○ Long road trip ○ Short flight to your destination?

15. WHICH IS MORE EXCITING? ○ GRAMMYS ○ OSCARS

16. Ever entered a competition? ○ No ○ Yes, _____

_____

17. VACATION IN ○ THE USA ○ AN EXOTIC LOCATION?

18. What would be a fun business to start?

_____

19. Chew gum? ○ No ○ Yes, I love

_____

20. Who's your favorite superhero?

NAME ON YOUR BIRTH CERTIFICATE?

1. DAY, DATE & TIME YOU WERE BORN?

2. SOMETHING MOST PEOPLE DON'T KNOW ABOUT YOU?

3. WHAT DO YOU DO WHEN YOU'RE

MAD?

• YELL • CRY • GET QUIET

4. WHO DO YOU SPILL YOUR GUTS TO?

5. • MAKE QUICK DECISIONS
   • THINK ABOUT IT
   • AVOID DECISION-MAKING?

6. ○ TACO ○ BURRITO ○ ENCHILADA ○ FAJITA?

SAUCE ME!

7. Which is worse? ○ Paper cut ○ Burning your tongue

8. LAST THING YOU WROTE ABOUT? _____

9. Are you a hat girl? ○ No ○ Yes, I own_____ hats.

10. What would you do with an extra hour every day?

11. What's a typical Saturday for you? _____

12. First word you said? _____

13. Weirdest thing in your backpack or bag?

14. ○ Early ○ Right on time ○ Late to class?

15. Best memory you have? _____

_____

16. What do you always lose? ○ socks ○ ponytail holders ○ pens

17. ○ Rays of sunshine on your face ○ Cool breeze in the shade?

18. Language you'd like to learn?

19. If you found $50, would you ○ save it ○ spend it ○ try to find its owner?

20. EVER FLOWN IN A HELICOPTER? ○ NO ○ YES, _____

coke or pepsi?

ALL THE NAMES YOU GO BY?

ONE WORD TO
DESCRIBE YOURSELF?

THREE WORDS TO DESCRIBE GIRLS?

1.

2.

3.

MOST MAGICAL?
- PEGASUS • UNICORN
- DRAGON • OTHER ↓

- ROCK STAR
- STARFISH
- SHOOTING STAR?

FAVORITE SONG FROM A MOVIE?

READ ANYTHING GOOD LATELY?
- NOT REALLY • OH YEAH, IT'S

- CHOCOLATE • PRETZELS
- CHOCOLATE-COVERED PRETZELS?

WHAT'S OUTSIDE THE WINDOW CLOSEST TO YOU?

CAN YOU WHISTLE A TUNE?
○ YES
○ A LITTLE BIT
○ NO

THREE WORDS TO DESCRIBE BOYS?
1.
2.
3.

WHAT KIND OF STUDENT ARE YOU?
○ GOOD ○ GREAT
○ COULD BE BETTER

○ MOUNTAIN CLIMBING
○ HIKING TRAILS
○ S'MORES AROUND A CAMPFIRE?

TRAMPOLINES?
○ YES, LOVE THEM!
○ NO WAY!

EVER BEEN PRANKED? ○ NO ○ YES,

WHO MAKES YOU LAUGH THE HARDEST?

WEIRDEST MOVIE YOU'VE SEEN?

SOMETHING YOU'RE OBSESSED WITH?

WHAT DRIVES YOU CRAZY?

WHAT MAKES YOU FEEL REALLY LOVED?

NAME

1. WHAT'S ON YOUR CALENDAR THIS WEEK?

2. LAST THING YOU COOKED, MICROWAVED, OR TOASTED?

3. FAVORITE
ROOM IN YOUR HOME?

4. HOW DO YOU LIKE TO
DECORATE?

5. WHAT'S YOUR FASHION STYLE?

6. EVER WEAR YOUR FRIENDS' CLOTHES? ○ NOT REALLY ○ ⊙ OH YEAH

7. SPRINKLES & GLITTER
   ○ MAKE EVERYTHING FUN ○ ARE ANNOYING & MESSY?

8. Who encourages you the most? _____

9. Staying organized ○ is so helpful ○ messes up creativity?

10. Something you wish you were good at? _____

_____

11. SOMETHING NEW YOU'VE LEARNED? _____

12. Favorite holiday treat? _____

13. Eggnog? ○ Love it! ○ So gross!

14. Celebrity wardrobe you'd love to borrow from?

_____

15. Are you squeamish? ○ Totally ○ Nah

16. ARE YOU AN ADVENTUROUS EATER? ○ YES ○ NO

17. CAMPING STYLE? ○ TENT ○ CABIN ○ RV

18. Ever encountered a wild animal?

○ No ○ Yes, _____

19. Favorite amusement park?

_____

20. Are you having a
○ good ○ bad ○ horrible hair day?

coke or pepsi?

NAME YOU WRITE ON NAMETAG?

?

1. WHAT WOULD YOU DO WITH $1,000 IN ONE DAY?

2. DO YOU LIKE BEING IN THE SPOTLIGHT?
- YES
- NO

3. WHAT MAKES YOU LOSE TRACK OF TIME?

4.
- SOUR CREAM
- BARBEQUE
- CHEDDAR
- OTHER
CHIPS?

5. WHAT DO YOU DO IN YOUR SPARE TIME?

MR. MEOW, WHAT SHOULD I WEAR TO THE DANCE?

6. DO YOU TALK TO YOUR PET LIKE IT'S A PERSON? ○ OF COURSE! ○ NAH

7. DO FRIENDS COUNT ON YOU FOR ○ PEP TALKS ○ REALITY CHECKS ○ SOME LAUGHS?

8. Fave game of all time? _____

9. Best band ever? _____

10. Favorite book character? _____

11. How many times do you hit Snooze in the morning? _____

12. FOOD YOU LOVE TO SMELL COOKING? _____

13. Where are you right now? _____

14. Where would you rather be? _____

15. Do you ○ think about the past ○ dream about the future more?

16. Have you ever been lost in a corn maze? ○ No ○ Yes!

17. Rather have a friend who ○ totally gets you ○ is tons of fun?

18. WHO DO YOU LOOK UP TO? ⟨_____⟩

19. Ever fallen asleep in the middle of something? ○ No ○ Yes,

20. Chocolate & ○ peanut butter ○ marshmallows ○ coconut?

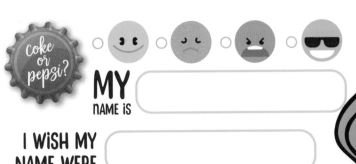

coke or pepsi?

MY name is

I WISH MY NAME WERE

LITTLE KIDS ARE
○ FUN
○ ANNOYING?

FAMOUS PERSON YOU WOULD TRADE PLACES WITH?

....

WHAT'S BETTER?
○ ASKING QUESTIONS
○ GIVING ANSWERS

FAMOUS PERSON YOU'D NEVER TRADE PLACES WITH?

....

EVER BEEN EMBARRASSED BY YOUR PARENTS?
● NO ● YES
☞

SMARTEST PERSON YOU KNOW?

● COMFY
● TRENDY
SHOES?

IF YOU COULD INVENT SOMETHING, WHAT WOULD IT BE?

RULES SHOULD BE
○ FOLLOWED ○ USED AS GUIDELINES ○ BROKEN?

WORST FASHION MISTAKE YOU'VE EVER MADE?

○ PAY NOW PLAY LATER
○ PLAY NOW PAY LATER?

STUDY
○ ALONE
○ WITH A FRIEND
○ IN A GROUP?

BEST THING ABOUT SCHOOL?

MOST ANNOYING THING ABOUT SCHOOL?

MOST OUTRAGEOUS THING YOU'VE EVER EATEN?

WRITE papers
• IN ADVANCE
• THE NIGHT BEFORE?

FIRST NAME

1. STORY BEHIND YOUR FIRST NAME? ● NO ● YES

2. IF YOU COULD GO TO ONLY ONE CONCERT THIS YEAR, WHICH WOULD IT BE?

3. ● PAY ATTENTION TO LYRICS
● JUST ROCK OUT TO THE MUSIC
● BOTH?

4. HOW WOULD YOUR FRIENDS DESCRIBE YOU?
● SWEET   ● RELIABLE   ● A LITTLE CRAY-CRAY?

5. EVER BEEN IN A PLAY? ● NO ● YES

6. Are you good at telling jokes? ○ Yes ○ No

7. Which would be fun to play? ○ Damsel in distress ○ Spy ○ Supervillain

8. Biggest question about life? _____

9. Have a fave cartoon? ○ Nope ○ Yep. _____

10. BEST CHARACTER iN AN ANiMATED MOViE? _____

11. Weirdest animal you've ever seen? _____

12. Fave clothing brand? ○ Nah ○ Yes, _____

13. ○ Cake ○ Cupcake? What kind?

_____

14. Fictional character you wish were real?

15. ○ STYLE OVER COMFORT ○ COMFORT OVER STYLE?

16. Fave beverage on ice?

_____

17. Tastiest frozen treat? _____

18. Better at speaking ○ to a crowd ○ one-on-one ○ to a group of friends?

19. What do your parents always bug you about? _____

_____

20. Dish you love to make?

coke or pepsi?

WHAT ARE YOUR iNiTiALS?

1. FAVORiTE KiND OF DOG?

2. DO YOUR MOViES NEED A HAPPY ENDiNG?
• NO • DEPENDS • ALWAYS

3. YOUR BEST PERSONALiTY TRAiT?

4. YOUR NOT-SO-AWESOME PERSONALiTY TRAiT?

5. WHO'S YOUR HERO?

6. ○ Love waking up to birds! ○ No, not the birds!

7. If you were a crayon, which color would you be?

8. What do you know a lot about? _____

9. What do you know nothing about? _____

10. ○ Board games ○ Bored with games?

11. Who taught you to tie your shoes? _____

12. MOST EMBARRASSING MOMENT EVER?

_____

13. Holidays with your family are ○ really fun ○ OK ○ kind of crazy?

14. FAVE THING YOU COULD GIVE UP FOR 1 YEAR?

_____

15. FAVE THING YOU COULD NOT GIVE UP FOR 1 YEAR?

_____

16. First thing you do in the morning?

_____

17. ○ Swiss cheese
○ Cheddar cheese
○ No cheese, please!

18. Last thing you do before bed?

_____

19. WHAT WOULD YOU LOVE TO DO BUT THINK YOU CAN'T?

_____

20. SPAGHETTI AND ○ MEATBALLS ○ CLAMS ○ OTHER _____ ?

FIRST, MIDDLE, & LAST NAME

○ SMALL TOWN
○ BIG CITY
GOTTA FAVE?

WHICH IS WORSE?
○ BRUSSELS SPROUTS ○ BROCCOLI?

○ **SWEET TASTING**
○ **TANGY FRO-YO?**
COOLEST ADULT YOU KNOW?

FAVE SPUDS?
○ FRENCH FRIES ○ BAKED
○ HOME FRIES ○ CHIPS

HOW DO YOU LIKE SPICY FOOD?
○ MILD ○ MEDIUM ○ KABOOM!

FAVORITE
GRADE IN SCHOOL?

FOREIGN FILMS?
○ YES, FUN!
○ NO, SUBTITLES
ARE ANNOYING!

WHAT DO YOU THINK OF WHEN YOU HEAR THE WORD ORANGE?

WHAT DO YOU THINK OF WHEN YOU SEE THE WORD RED?

OPEN UMBRELLAS INDOORS?
○ YES ○ NO

EVER SNORT WHEN YOU LAUGH?
○ HA, YES! ○ NAH

EVER FALLEN DOWN IN PUBLIC?
○ YES ○ NO

○ SCRAMBLED
○ HARD BOILED
○ FRIED
○ NO EGGS?

EASIEST PERSON TO BUY A GIFT FOR?

MOST PEACEFUL COLOR?

WHICH IS WORSE?
○ NEVER BEING ABLE TO TEXT
○ NEVER BEING ABLE TO CALL

READ INSTRUCTIONS?
○ ALWAYS ○ SOMETIMES ○ NEVER!

WALK UNDER LADDERS?
○ NO WAY! ○ YEP

EVER FORGOTTEN TO REMOVE A PRICE TAG FROM YOUR CLOTHES?
yes no

coke or pepsi?

NAME

1. WHAT'S YOUR RINGTONE?

2. MOST POPULAR COLOR IN YOUR CLOSET?

3. LAST THING YOU TOOK A PHOTO OF?

4. HOW DID YOU MEET YOUR BFF?

5. BANANA · & P-NUT BUTTER · NUT BREAD · CREAM PIE?

6. Ice skating is ○ so fun ○ OK ○ an accident waiting to happen?

7. Movie with the best ending? _____

8. Movie with the worst ending? _____

9. ○ Grilled ○ Roasted ○ Fried ○ Tofu chicken?

10. Fave TV actress? _____

11. Fave TV actor? _____

12. Fave song right now?

13. HARD FOR YOU TO SAY YOU'RE WRONG? ○ YES ○ WITH SOME PEOPLE ○ NOT REALLY

14. ○ Thick ○ Thin ○ Sicilian ○ Stuffed pizza?

15. Least favorite subject in school? _____

16. EVER GO THRU A "DO NOT ENTER" DOOR? ○ YES ○ NO

17. Are you usually too ○ hot ○ cold?

18. Allergic to anything? ○ No ○ Yes, _____

19. BEST-EVER SANDWICH? _____

20. Fashion trend you love right now?

coke or pepsi?

NAME [   ]

1. Prefer shopping ○ online ○ in person?

2. WOULD YOU RATHER BE ○ MAGICAL ○ A MUGGLE?

3. WORST THING YOU'VE EVER EATEN? _____

4. ○ Shoestring ○ Crinkle cut ○ Steak ○ Waffle fries?

5. ○ Pencil ○ Pen ○ Keyboard?

6. Best show on TV? _____

7. Worst show on TV? _____

8. WHAT DO YOU DO WHEN NO ONE ELSE IS AROUND? _____

9. ○ Plain ○ Whole grain ○ Cinnamon swirl ○ Everything bagel?

10. ○ Regular ○ Berry ○ Chive ○ Other _____ cream cheese on a bagel?

11. Favorite number? _____ Why? _____

12. EXOTIC ANIMAL YOU'D LOVE AS A PET? _____

13. Last word you looked up in a dictionary? _____

14. FASHION ACCESSORY THAT'S SO YOU? _____

15. ○ Kitten ○ puppy videos?

16. ○ Giving ○ Receiving gifts is awesome!

17. Best advice you've ever received? _____

18. Super sense you'd love to have? ○ Hearing ○ Sight ○ Smell

19. Are you brave? ○ absolutely ○ sometimes ○ no

20. Vacay you'd ♥ to take? _____

movie you can watch over and over again?

NAME YOUR FRIENDS CALL YOU?

1. SONG YOU GET STUCK iN YOUR HEAD?

2. IF YOU WERE A DJ, WHAT KiND OF MUSiC WOULD YOU PLAY?

3. FAVE WAY TO DiSCOVER NEW MUSiC?

4. SONG YOU ALWAYS GET UP AND DANCE TO?

5. SONG YOU CAN'T STAND?

6. Fave text abbreviation?

7. Least fave text abbreviation?

8. WEAR GREEN ON ST. PATRICK'S DAY?
○ ALWAYS ○ SOMETIMES ○ NEVER

9. One word to describe your BFF?

_____

10. WHAT'S MORE FUN? ○ SLEEPOVER ○ PARTY

11. DO YOU KNOW HOW TO YO-YO?
○ YES ○ KIND OF ○ NO

12. ○ Picnic in the park ○ Fun night out?

13. Worst chore ever? _____

14. Watch anything last night? ○ No ○ Yes, _____

15. Playground game you miss? _____

16. Are you more ○ emotional ○ logical ○ 50/50?

17. WOULD YOU DESCRIBE YOURSELF AS ○ EXTROVERTED ○ INTROVERTED ○ IN THE MIDDLE?

18. How would your family describe you? _____

_____

19. CELEBRITY YOU'RE THE MOST LIKE? _____

20. If you could, what would you splurge on? _____

_____

coke or pepsi?

NAME [   ]

1. NAME YOU WISH YOU HAD? [   ]

2. ○ I'M THE QUEEN OF
   ○ ENOUGH WITH THE
   ○ OTHER _____
   SELFIES?

3. ○ MAC ○ PC?

CHECK OUT MY NEW SHADES!

4. IF YOUR PET COULD TALK, WHAT 3 QUESTIONS WOULD YOU ASK iT?

[   ]

[   ]

[   ]

5. DOES YOUR PET HAVE A COOL TRICK OR SWEET HABiT?

[   ]

6. CELEB YOU'D LOVE AS YOUR OTHER BFF? _____

7. Vacation ○ in the big city   ○ warm beach ○ another country?

8. Family's favorite meal? _____

9. Waffles with ○ strawberries & whipped cream ○ butter & maple syrup?

10. Best thing on your bedroom walls? _____

11. Ever been a member of a fan club? ○ No ○ Yes, _____

12. DO YOU HAVE A CELEBRITY AUTOGRAPH? ○ NO ○ YES, _____

13. Favorite song to sing with friends?

14. ○ Fast food   ○ Themed restaurant   ○ Fine dining?

15. FAVE VEGGIE?

16. Do your friends love your
○ sense of humor
○ talent
○ style?

17. Poetry is
○ awesome
○ OK
○ so boring?

18. Tell people there's food stuck in their teeth?
○ Never ○ Depends ○ Always

19. Something you do really fast? _____

20. Is your dream machine a(n)
○ limo with driver ○ SUV
○ sports car ○ hybrid?

coke or pepsi?

NAME

WHO HAS IT EASIER?
- GIRLS
- BOYS

☞ WHY?

HOW MANY PAIRS OF SHOES DO YOU OWN?
- NOT ENOUGH
- JUST RIGHT
- TOO MANY!

SOMETHING YOU ♥ THAT MOST PEOPLE HATE?

WHAT'S YOUR BEST HABIT?

STUDY
- IN A QUIET PLACE
- WITH MUSIC IN MY EARS
- WITH TV ON?

HOW ARE YOU WHEN WAITING
iN LONG LINES?
○ COOL ○ IRRITATED ○ I WALK AWAY!

EVER BEEN ON TV?
○ NOPE ○ YES,
_____

FAVE SNEAKER COLOR?
○ ● ○ ● ○ ● ○ ● ○ ●
OTHER _____

TV SHOW THAT WOULD
BE FUN TO ⭐ iN?
_____

LAST SiTCH WHICH REALLY UPSET YOU?
_____

EVER BELIEVE
A MONSTER
WAS UNDER
YOUR BED?
○ YES
○ NO

FAVE FREE-TIME THING TO DO?
_____

LAST MOVIE
YOU SAW?
_____

FAVE JUNK FOOD?
_____

FAVE SUPER HEALTHY FOOD?
_____

HARD
TO SAY
YOU'RE
SORRY?
● YES
● SOMETIMES
● NO

MOST BORING BOOK YOU'VE EVER READ?
_____

GO-TO MOVIE FOOD?
○ POPCORN ○ TWIZZLERS
○ NACHOS ○ OTHER

6. Favorite craft to make? _____

7. SCARED OF HEIGHTS? ○ YES! ○ NO ○ DEPENDS HOW HIGH.

8. Scared of spiders? ○ Ahh! Yes! ○ Nope

9. __ Finding a leprechaun __ Finding his pot of gold?

10. ○ Chocolate cake with chocolate ganache ○ Angel food cake with berries?

11. Jewelry you always wear? _____

12. Word you always misspell? _____

13. What or who totally amazes you?

14. ○ Long road trip ○ Short flight to your destination?

15. WHICH IS MORE EXCITING? ○ GRAMMYS ○ OSCARS

16. Ever entered a competition? ○ No ○ Yes, _____

_____

17. VACATION IN ○ THE USA ○ AN EXOTIC LOCATION?

18. What would be a fun business to start?

_____

19. Chew gum? ○ No ○ Yes, I love

_____

20. Who's your favorite superhero?

NAME ON YOUR BIRTH CERTIFICATE?

1. DAY, DATE & TIME YOU WERE BORN?

2. SOMETHING MOST PEOPLE DON'T KNOW ABOUT YOU?

3. WHAT DO YOU DO WHEN YOU'RE

MAD?

• YELL • CRY • GET QUIET

4. WHO DO YOU SPILL YOUR GUTS TO?

5.  • MAKE QUICK DECISIONS
• THINK ABOUT IT
• AVOID DECISION-MAKING?

6. ○ TACO ○ BURRITO ○ ENCHILADA ○ FAJITA?

SAUCE ME!

7. Which is worse? ○ Paper cut ○ Burning your tongue

8. LAST THING YOU WROTE ABOUT? _____

9. Are you a hat girl? ○ No ○ Yes, I own _____ hats.

10. **What would you do with an extra hour every day?**

11. What's a typical Saturday for you? _____

12. First word you said? _____

13. Weirdest thing in your backpack or bag?

14. ○ **Early** ○ **Right on time** ○ **Late to class?**

15. Best memory you have? _____

_____

16. **What do you always lose?** ○ socks ○ ponytail holders ○ pens

17. ○ Rays of sunshine on your face ○ Cool breeze in the shade?

18. *Language you'd like to learn?*

19. If you found $50, would you ○ save it ○ spend it ○ try to find its owner?

20. EVER FLOWN IN A HELICOPTER? ○ NO ○ YES, _____

WHAT'S GOING ON IN THAT BEAUTIFUL BRAIN OF YOURS?

LET US KNOW COKE-OR-PEPSI GIRL!

Write to us!

MICKEY & CHERYL
FINE PRINT PUBLISHING COMPANY
PO BOX 916401
LONGWOOD, FL 32791-6401

OU LOVE THiS BOOK, CHECK OUT THESE

Coke or Pepsi?

BOOKS!